EASIEST 5-FINGER PIANO COLLECTION

Big Chart Hits

15 top chart hits arranged for 5-finger piano

Wise Publications
part of The Music Sales Group
London / New York / Paris / Sydney / Copenhagen / Berlin / Madrid / Tokyo

SOMEONE LIKE YOU (Adele)

Words & Music by Adele Adkins & Daniel Wilson

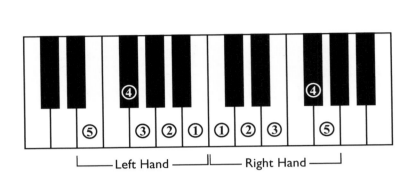

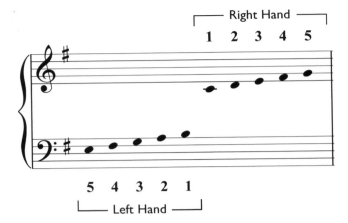

Never mind,___ I'll find some-one like

you.___ I wish noth-ing but___ the

best for you two. Don't for -

THE EDGE OF GLORY (Lady Gaga)

Words & Music by Fernando Garibay, Stefani Germanotta & Paul Blair

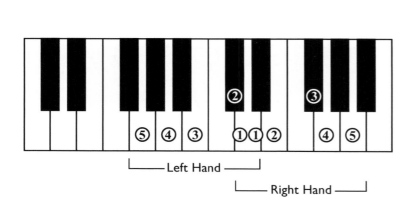

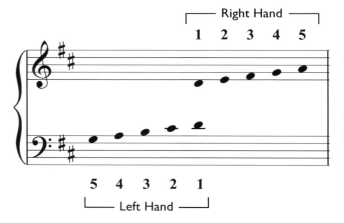

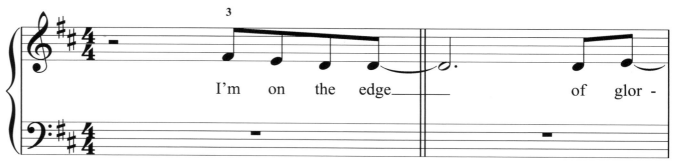

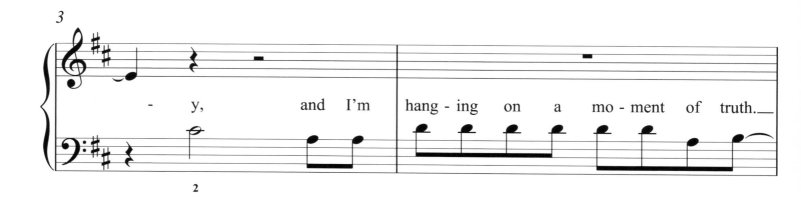

MARRY YOU (Bruno Mars)

Words & Music by Ari Levine, Peter Hernandez & Phillip Lawrence

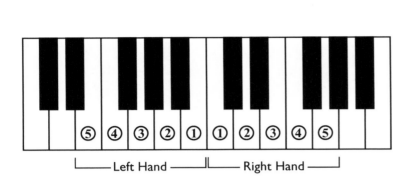

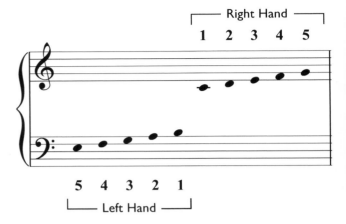

Enthusiastically ♩ = 138

Don't say no, no, no, no, no; just say

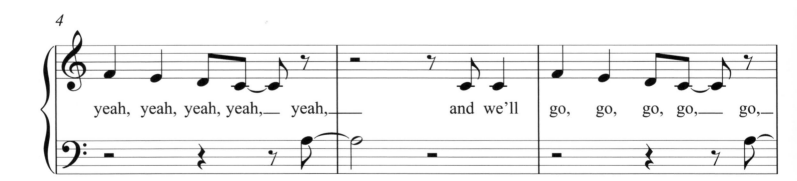

yeah, yeah, yeah, yeah, yeah, and we'll go, go, go, go, go,

if you're read - y, like I'm read - y. Yes, it's a

RIVIERA LIFE (Caro Emerald)

Words & Music by David Schreurs, Vincent Degiorgio, Willem Rozeboom & Jan van Wieringen

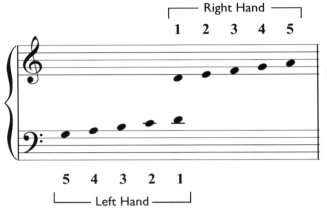

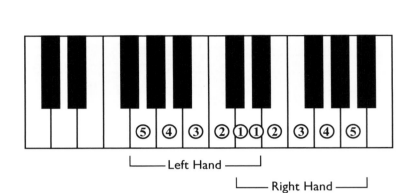

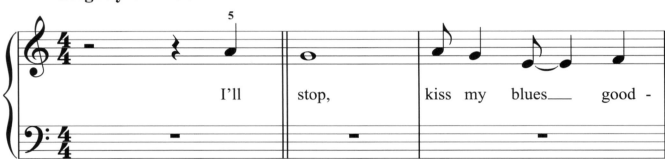

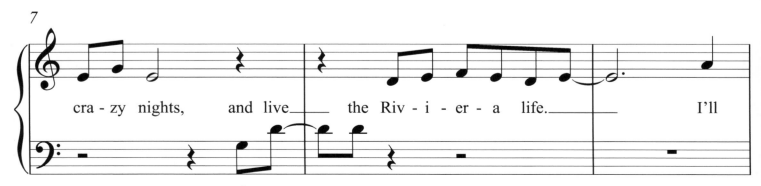

BEST THING I NEVER HAD (Beyoncé)

Words & Music by Beyoncé Knowles, Kenneth Edmonds, Antonio Dixon, Patrick Smith, Larry Griffin,
Caleb McCampbell & Robert Taylor

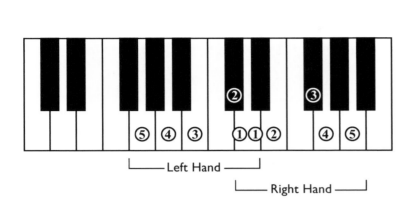

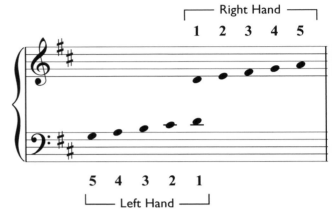

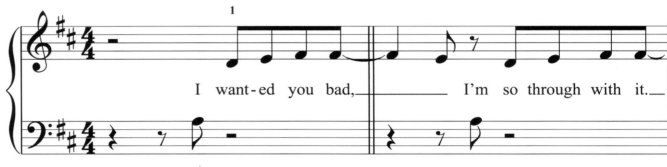

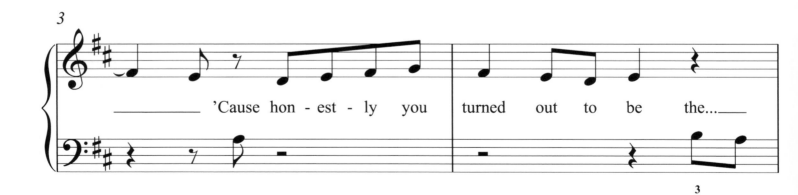

SET FIRE TO THE RAIN (Adele)

Words & Music by Fraser Smith & Adele Adkins

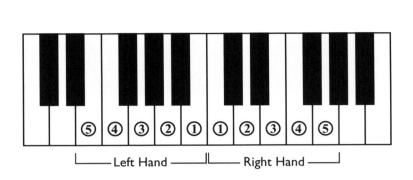

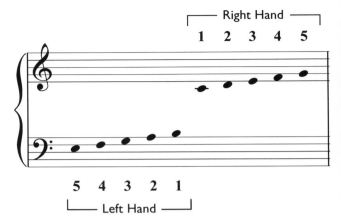

Powerfully ♩ = 108

'Cause there's a   side   to   you   that   I

nev - er knew, nev - er knew; all   the   things   you'd   say,   they   were

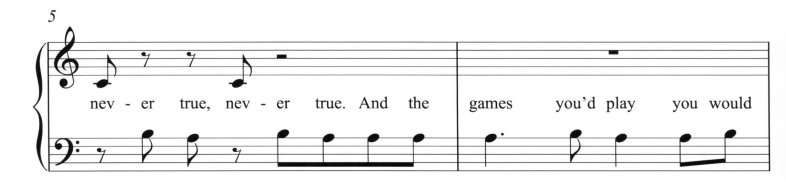

nev - er true, nev - er true. And   the   games   you'd   play   you   would

CALIFORNIA KING BED (Rihanna)

Words & Music by Jermaine Jackson, Priscilla Hamilton, Andrew Harr & Alexander Delicata

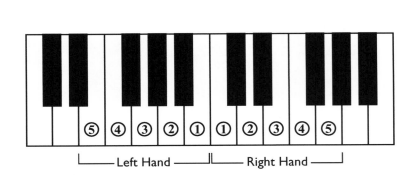

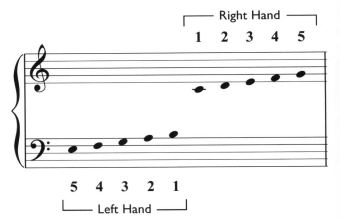

MR MEDICINE (Eliza Doolittle)

Words & Music by John Beck, Steven Chrisanthon & Eliza Caird

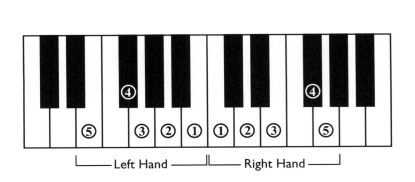

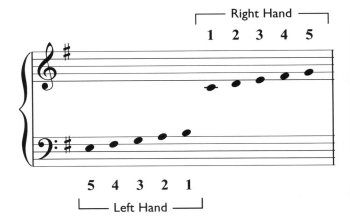

With a bounce ♩ = 92

Oh, Mis - ter Med - i - cine, oh, Mis - ter Med - i - cine.

Oh, Mis - ter Med - i - cine,___ I will take

an - y - thing.___ What do you rec - om - mend?___ Oh, Mis - ter

Med - i - cine,___   I need my   vit - a - mins;___   will I feel

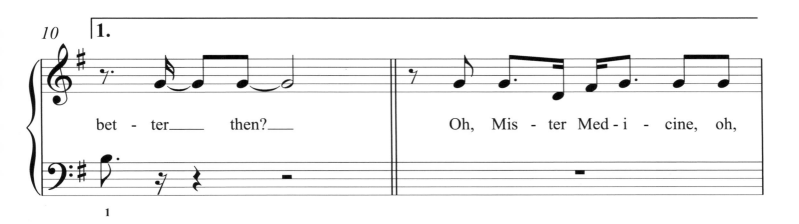

1.

bet - ter____ then?____   Oh, Mis - ter Med - i - cine, oh,

1

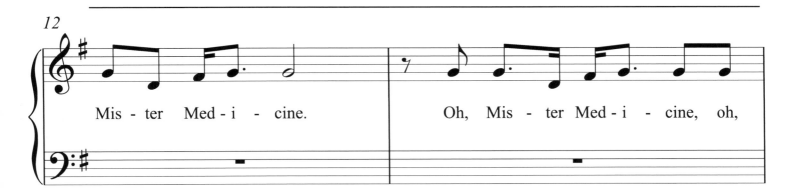

Mis - ter Med - i - cine.   Oh, Mis - ter Med - i - cine, oh,

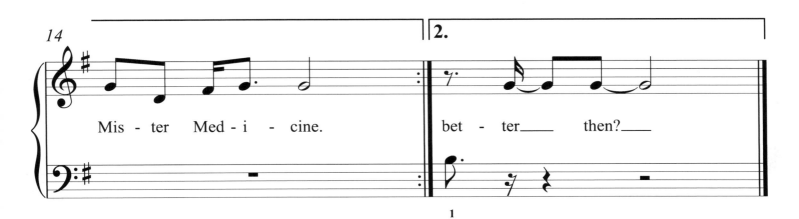

2.

Mis - ter Med - i - cine.   bet - ter____ then?____

1

LOVE GOES DOWN (Plan B)

Words & Music by Benjamin Drew, Eric Appapoulay, Richard Cassell & Tom Goss

Tenderly ♩ = 92

I re-mem-ber when I_____ was
All of_____ the things we_____ both

young, and so were you.
said we would nev-er do.

But look at how times have

changed, ba-by;___ you - oo - oo know___

I,_____ I could nev-er say no, ba-by.___

PACK UP (Eliza Doolittle)

Words & Music by Tim Woodcock, Matthew Prime, Felix Powell, Eliza Caird & George Asaf

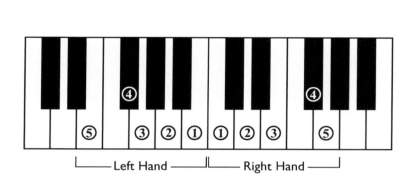

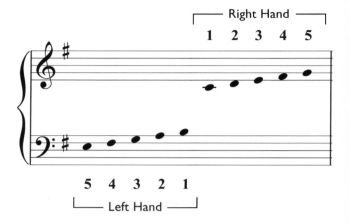

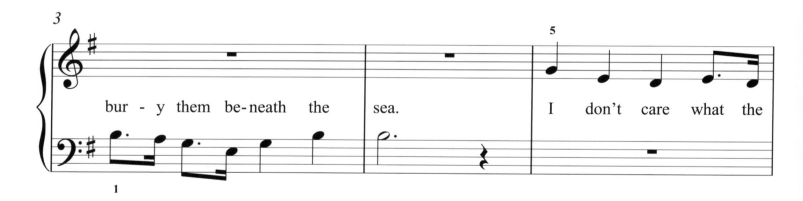

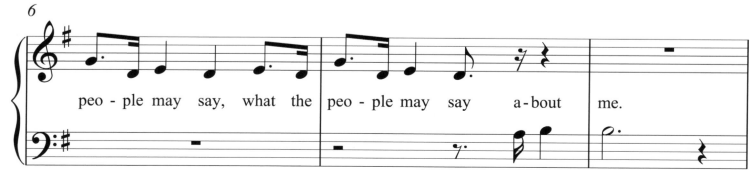

IT'S OK (Cee Lo Green)

Words & Music by Thomas Callaway, Hitesh Ceon, Kim Ofstad, Noel Fisher, Helgi Hübner,
Tshawe Baqwa & Yosef Wolde-Mariam

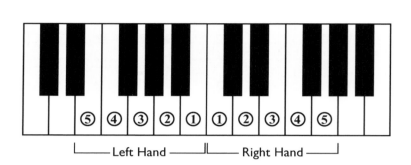

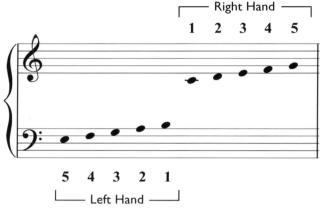

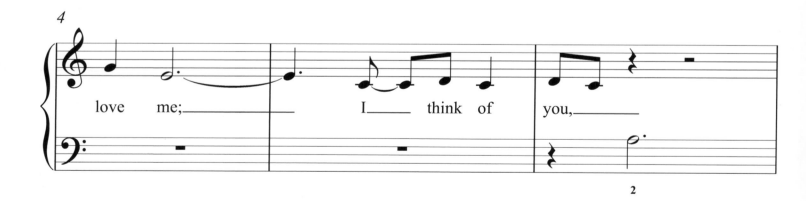

to say____ that you love me;_____ _____ I____ think of

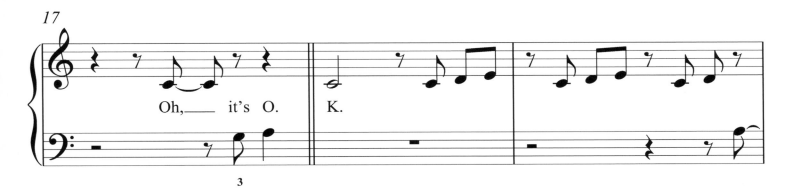

you,_____ still____ think of you._____

2

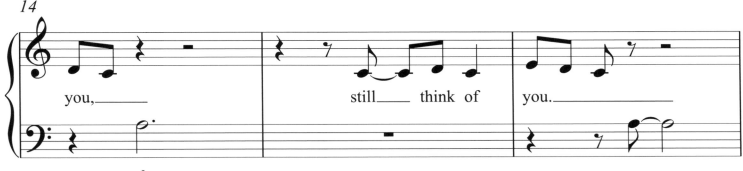

Oh,____ it's O. K.

3

2   1
4   3

2   1
4   3

PRICE TAG (Jessie J)

Words & Music by Lukasz Gottwald, Claude Kelly, Bobby Ray Simmons & Jessica Cornish

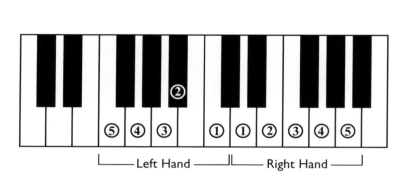

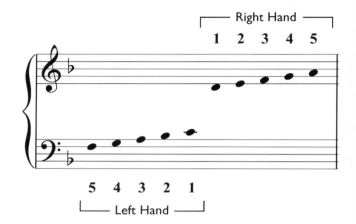

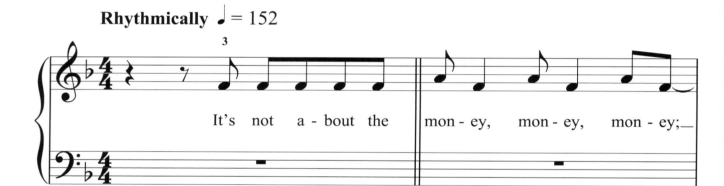

It's not a-bout the mon-ey, mon-ey, mon-ey;

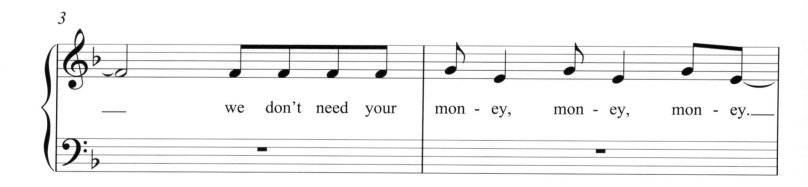

we don't need your mon-ey, mon-ey, mon-ey.

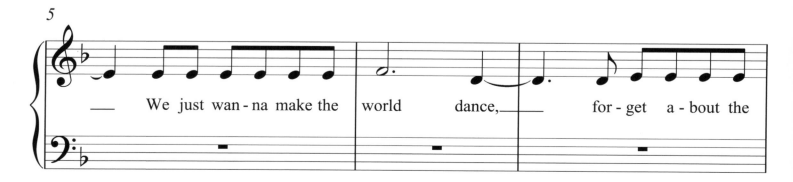

We just wan-na make the world dance, for-get a-bout the

price - tag.___ Ain't a - bout the cha - ching,___

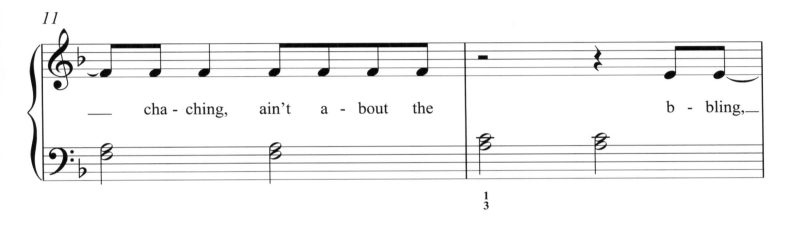

___ cha - ching, ain't a - bout the b - bling,___

___ b - bling. Wan - na make the world dance,___

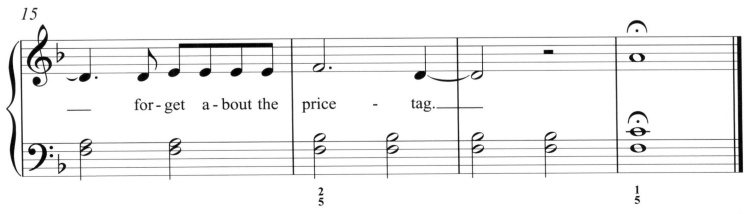

___ for - get a - bout the price - tag.___

ET (Katy Perry)

Words & Music by Max Martin, Lukasz Gottwald, Joshua Coleman & Katy Perry

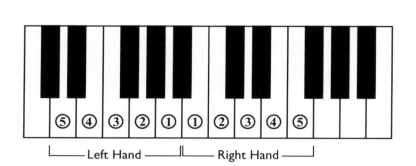

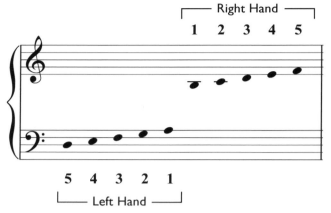

Robotically ♩ = 138

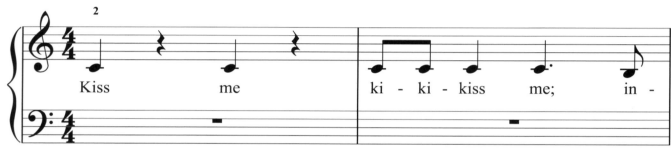

Kiss me ki - ki - kiss me; in -

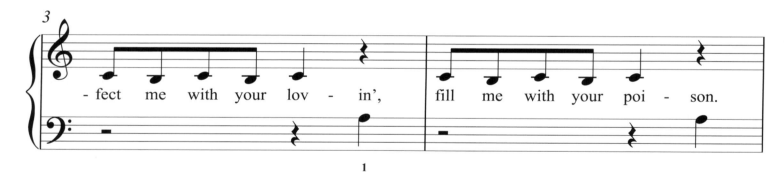

- fect me with your lov - in', fill me with your poi - son.

Take me ta - ta - take me; wan - na be your vic - tim,

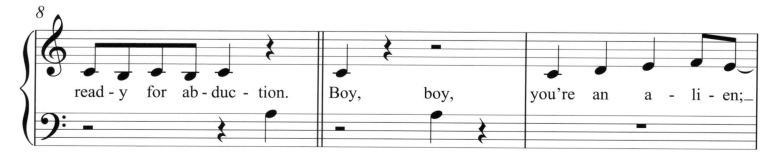

read - y for ab - duc - tion. Boy, boy, you're an a - li - en;

JUST THE WAY YOU ARE (Bruno Mars)

Words & Music by Ari Levine, Bruno Mars, Philip Lawrence, Peter Hernandez, Khari Cain & Khalil Walton

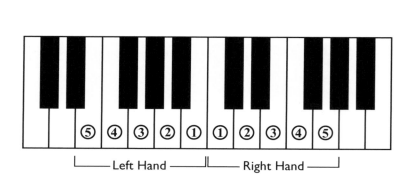

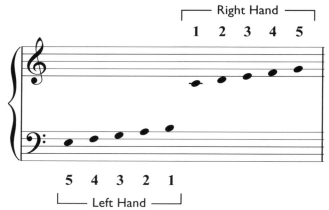

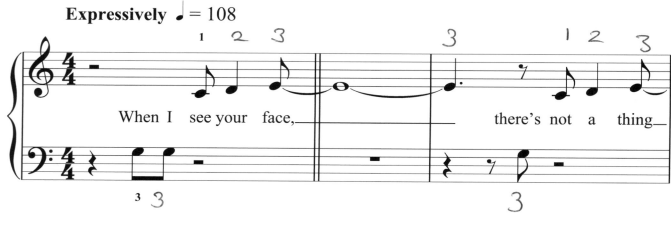

When I see your face,____ there's not a thing___

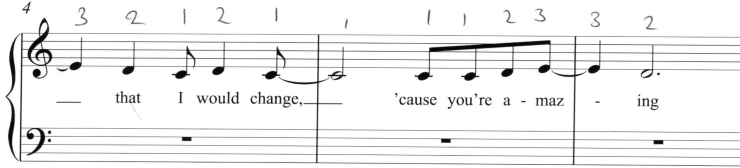

___ that I would change,___ 'cause you're a - maz - ing

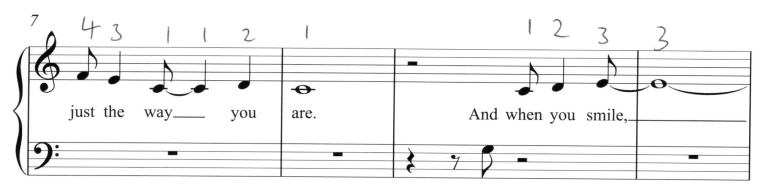

just the way___ you are. And when you smile,___

3

LAST FRIDAY NIGHT (Katy Perry)

Words & Music by Max Martin, Lukasz Gottwald, Bonnie McKee & Katy Perry

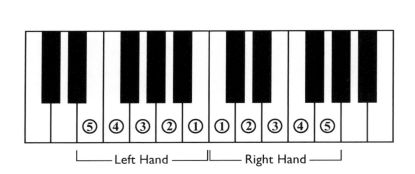

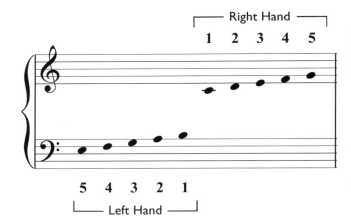

Lightly ♩ = 116

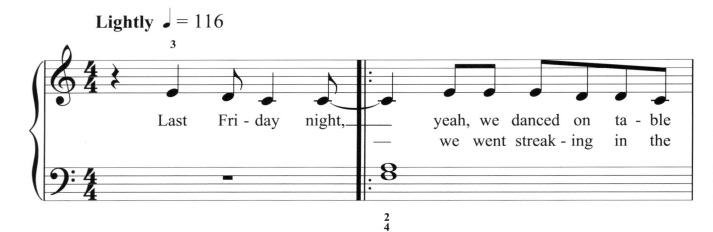

Last Fri-day night,— yeah, we danced on ta-ble
— we went streak-ing in the

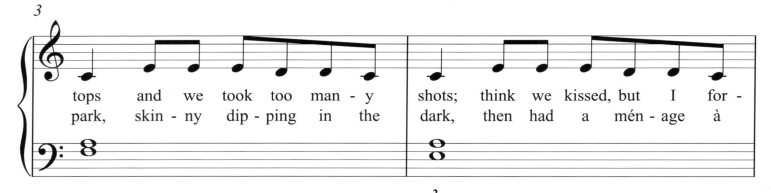

tops and we took too man-y shots; think we kissed, but I for-
park, skin-ny dip-ping in the dark, then had a mén-age à

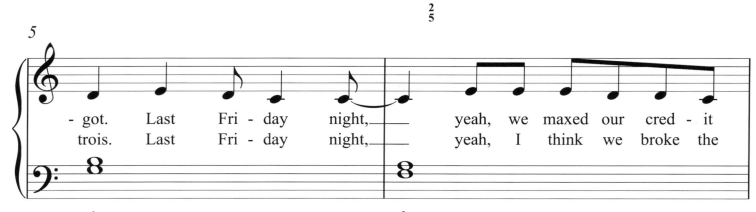

-got. Last Fri-day night,— yeah, we maxed our cred-it
trois. Last Fri-day night,— yeah, I think we broke the

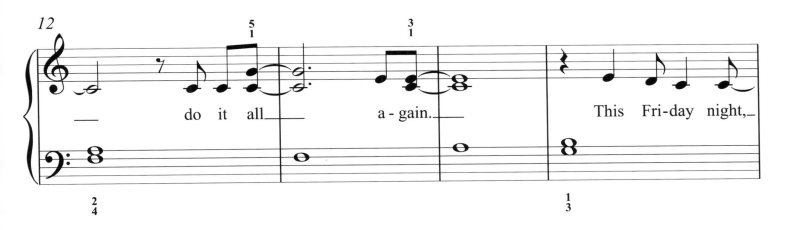

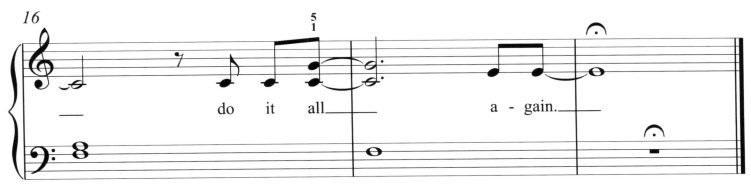

EASIEST 5-FINGER PIANO COLLECTION
ALSO AVAILABLE IN THE SERIES...

Abba
A great collection of 15 classic Abba hits, including 'Dancing Queen', 'Fernando', 'Take A Chance On Me' and 'Thank You For The Music'.
AM998404

Ballads
A superb collection of 15 well-known ballads, including 'Fix You', 'I Have A Dream', 'Let It Be' and 'What A Wonderful World'.
AM995346

The Beatles
15 classic Beatles hits including 'All My Loving', 'Hey Jude', 'She Loves You' and 'Yellow Submarine'.
NO91322

New Chart Hits
15 popular chart hits including 'Russian Roulette', 'Just Dance', 'Bad Boys', 'Don't Stop Believin'' and 'Cry Me Out'.
AM1001077

Classical Favourites
15 classical pieces including 'Jupiter' (Holst), 'Lullaby' (Brahms), 'Minuet In G' (J. S. Bach) and 'Spring' (Vivaldi).
AM998393

Film Songs
15 great film songs including 'Breaking Free', 'Don't Worry, Be Happy', 'Somewhere Out There' and 'You've Got A Friend In Me'.
AM995335

Showtunes
15 great showtunes including 'Any Dream Will Do', 'Circle Of Life', 'Mamma Mia' and 'My Favourite Things'.
AM995324

Today's Hits
15 of today's current chart hits including 'Hallelujah', 'Human', 'If I Were A Boy' and 'Viva La Vida'.
AM998415

Download to your computer a set of piano accompaniments for this *Big Chart Hits* edition
(to be played by a teacher/parent).
Visit: **www.hybridpublications.com**
Registration is free and easy.
Your registration code is BR376

Published by
Wise Publications
14-15 Berners Street,
London W1T 3LJ, UK.

Exclusive Distributors:
Music Sales Limited
Distribution Centre, Newmarket Road,
Bury St Edmunds, Suffolk IP33 3YB, UK.
Music Sales Pty Limited
20 Resolution Drive, Caringbah,
NSW 2229, Australia.

Order No. AM1003926
ISBN 978-1-78038-274-6
This book © Copyright 2011 Wise Publications,
a division of Music Sales Limited.

Edited by Jenni Norey.
Arranged by Chris Hussey.
Music processed by Camden Music Services.

Printed in the EU.

Your Guarantee of Quality
As publishers, we strive to produce every book to the highest commercial standards. This book has been carefully designed to minimise awkward page turns and to make playing from it a real pleasure. Particular care has been given to specifying acid-free, neutral-sized paper made from pulps which have not been elemental chlorine bleached. This pulp is from farmed sustainable forests and was produced with special regard for the environment. Throughout, the printing and binding have been planned to ensure a sturdy, attractive publication which should give years of enjoyment. If your copy fails to meet our high standards, please inform us and we will gladly replace it.

www.musicsales.com